VOICE for LIFE

SINGER'S WORKBOOK 2: LIGHT BLUE LEVEL

CONTENTS

This book belongs to

_____

of

_____ choir.

VOICE
for LIFE

Project editor: Tim Ruffer
Written and edited by Catherine Duffy, Anthony Marks and Leah Perona–Wright
This edition fully revised and updated by Anthony Marks

Voice for Life was developed by Leah Perona–Wright in consultation with experienced practitioners from across the UK and beyond. These include: Gordon Appleton, Colin Baldy, Roger Brice, Chris Broughton, Lesley Cooper, June Cox, Colin Davey, Paul Ellis, Peter Futcher, Susan Gardner, Ameral Gunson, John Harper, Esther Jones, Sally Leeming, Hilary Llystyn Jones, Sue Moore, David Ogden, Keith Roberts, Sheila Robertson, Ben Saunders, John Wardle, Alistair Warwick, Geoff Weaver and Jenevora Williams. We are grateful for their contributions.

Design and layout: Anthony Marks and Catherine Duffy
Music origination: Leah Perona–Wright and Anthony Marks
Illustrations: Hilary Perona–Wright
Editorial assistance: Julian Elloway and Sally Ruffer

Printed in Great Britain by Caligraving Ltd, Thetford

ISBN 978-0-85402-212-0

THE ROYAL SCHOOL OF CHURCH MUSIC
19 The Close, Salisbury, Wiltshire, SP1 2EB
Tel: +44 (0)1722 424848   Fax: +44 (0)1722 424849
E-mail: education@rscm.com Website: www.rscm.com
Registered charity no. 312828

Distributed exclusively in North America by GIA Publications, Inc.
7404 S. Mason Ave., Chicago, IL 60638
Toll free: 800 442 1358   Website: www.giamusic.com

Welcome to the Light Blue level of *Voice for Life*. It is designed to help you discover more about what your voice can do and improve further as a singer. It will increase your knowledge and understanding of music, and help you progress as a member of your choir.

This workbook will help you to practise singing and work on your musical knowledge at home. Your choir director will need to help you through it – don't try to finish the whole book on your own in a week! He or she may want to introduce a new topic to you before you do the work set in this book. Your choir director will want to make sure you understand each section before you move on to the next. He or she will want to set you tasks to complete at home and check your answers.

An important part of *Voice for Life* is learning to make the most of your voice. To develop and improve their singing, all singers need to practise regularly, both on their own and with their choir. This workbook contains vocal exercises for you to do at home. You will also need to take good care of your voice at all times. There are tips on voice care throughout this book.

There are puzzles and exercises to complete in your own time in this book. But being a member of a choir is also about being part of a team. You will learn about becoming a good team member and making the best contribution you can to your choir. You will also learn about the role of your choir in your church or school and in your wider community.

To complete the Light Blue level of *Voice for Life* you have to meet the targets on pages 44–46. Some of the targets involve demonstrating your knowledge at rehearsals, services or events when you sing in the choir. Others are things you can do in your own time. When you complete each target your choir director will sign a box. Inside the back cover of this workbook you can find out what happens when you complete all the targets. If you want to find anything else in this book, look at the index of music theory terms on pages 42–43, or the general index on pages 47–48.

Enjoy *Voice for Life!*

Andrew Reid
Director, RSCM

Icons The icons in this book tell you to:

Read this before going further	Try a vocal or physical exercise	Sing something
Think about something	Write an answer in the box	Tick when you have finished an activity

Posture

 You use your whole body when you sing. It is your musical instrument. This means that your posture (how you stand or sit) affects your singing voice. Good posture helps you to sing well.

Standing to sing
You should have:

- a tall posture with a straight back and an upright head

- relaxed shoulders

- relaxed knees

- your weight distributed evenly on both feet

- your feet slightly apart and firmly on the ground

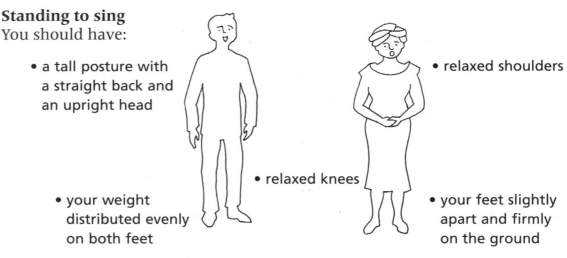

Some ways of standing can make your body tense, as your muscles have to work harder to keep you upright and balanced. They may also restrict your breathing, which affects the sound of your voice. Try to avoid:

- a slumped back
- standing with your head on one side
- locked knees (pushed back too far)
- standing with your feet together
- standing with your weight on one leg
- hunched or raised shoulders

Look at the pictures below. What is wrong with the way these singers are standing? Write your answers in the boxes.

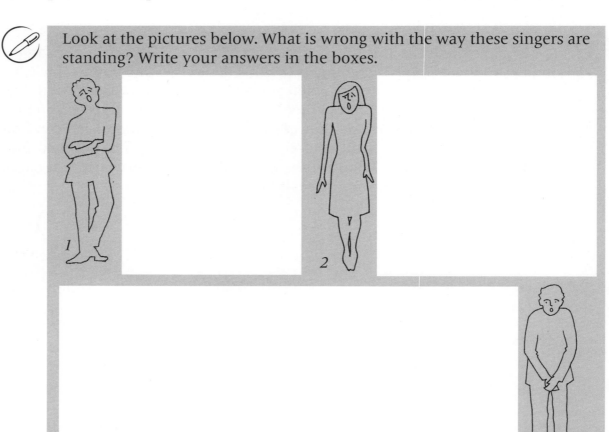

Look at yourself in a mirror, or ask a friend or your choir trainer to look at your posture when you stand. Compare your posture with the good and bad postures opposite. What is good about the way you stand?

What do you or your choir trainer think you need to work on?

 Sitting to sing
It is usually better to stand than sit while singing, but if you have good posture you can still sing well when sitting. You should have:

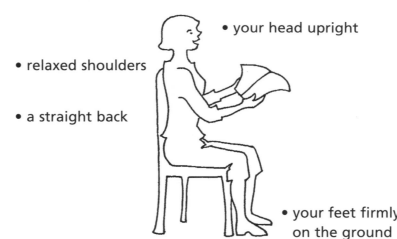

• your head upright

• relaxed shoulders

• a straight back

• your feet firmly on the ground

 Some positions or ways of sitting may restrict your breathing or make your throat tense. This may have a bad effect on your voice. If possible, try to avoid:

• hunching your back or slumping in your seat

• hunched shoulders, neck or upper body

• crossing your legs (this makes your body twist and may make you slump)

 VOICE CARE TIP
Never chew gum or sweets during a rehearsal or performance.
You won't be able to sing at your best, and you could choke.

Posture

 Look at the pictures below. What is wrong with the way these singers are sitting?

 Look at yourself in a mirror, or ask a friend or your choir trainer to look at your posture when you sit. Compare your posture with the pictures above and on the previous page. What is good about the way you sit?

What do you or your choir trainer think you need to work on?

 To achieve the 'Posture' target for Light Blue (page 44), you need to demonstrate good posture consistently during rehearsals and performances.

At first you will need to think about your posture often. Make sure you are standing or sitting well wherever you are – at the bus-stop, at your desk – not just when singing. Soon you will do this without thinking about it.

Breathing is automatic, and normally you do not think about it. But when you sing, you need to think about breathing because you do it in a different way. How you breathe affects all aspects of your voice. If you practise it regularly, you will soon notice a difference in your singing. The exercises below will help you to control your breath. Before you start, check your posture.

 1) Breathe in through your nose
Breathe out. Then take in a long deep breath through your nose. Hold it gently, then allow the breath to come out through your mouth in a gentle sigh.

 2) Breathe in through your mouth
When you can do (1) above without any tension in your throat or body, try breathing in and out through your mouth. Make sure your throat is open.

 3) Control your breath with a hiss
Breathe in slowly through your nose while you count to three. Breathe out slowly through your mouth while you count to three, making a hissing noise.

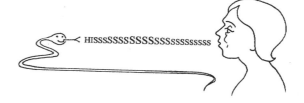

Breathe in and hiss out again. Increase the count to four, then five. If your neck and throat get tense, go back to a lower count and practise that a few times.

 4) Control your breath with a hum
Breathe in slowly while counting three, then hum a low note while counting three. Make sure the note you hum is even in tone – the same volume from beginning to end.

Then increase the count to four, then five. Make sure that the humming remains even in volume each time.

 5) Developing breath control and even tone
When you can produce an even hum for (4) above, practise the same exercise again but instead of humming, sing the note to 'oo' or 'ah'. Remember to keep the volume even each time.

 While you do the exercises above, think about the following:

- There should be no sound when you breathe in. If your breath is noisy, your neck and throat are probably tense.

- Your shoulders should not rise as you breathe in or fall as you breathe out. They should stay relaxed and still.

 If you get nervous when you sing, it may affect your breathing. If this happens, check your posture and try to relax. Breathe slowly and steadily: in to a count of four, then out to a count of four. Keep your throat open and relaxed.

Tone and range

How your voice works

Your voice starts in a part of your throat called the **larynx** (say *LAR-rinks*). It contains tiny flaps of skin called **vocal folds**. When your breath passes over them, they vibrate. Put your hands or fingers gently on your throat while you speak or sing to feel these vibrations. They create the sound of your voice.

Resonance

The vibrations in your larynx make other parts of your body vibrate too. This makes the sound louder. Singers call this **resonance**. Try touching other areas of your face and body (such as your cheeks, jaw and nose) while humming. Can you feel the vibrations in some of these places?

The main areas of resonance are the throat, mouth, nose, head, chest and stomach. Experiment with different sounds like high-pitched sirens (see opposite), or low growling. With each sound you make, feel the vibrations in different parts of your body.

Tone

Singers use the word **tone** to talk about how a voice resonates and how even it is. Tone depends on many things, like posture and breathing. The information and exercises on pages 4–9 will improve your posture and breath control.

But tone is also affected by how comfortable your voice is when you sing. If you try to sing notes that are too high or low for your voice, tension will harm your tone. It is important to find a comfortable place for your voice.

Finding a comfortable note

Laugh energetically ('ha! ha! ha!'). Now do this again, but this time, hold the 'ah' sound of the final 'ha!' The note you are now singing will be in a comfortable part of your voice. Try to remember this note. Find it on an instrument, then write it on the staff below. (For more about this, see pages 14–15, or ask your choir trainer to help you write it down.)

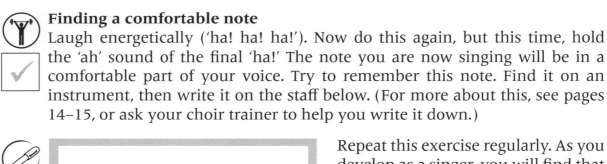

Repeat this exercise regularly. As you develop as a singer, you will find that the note at the end of your laugh will change. Write in the other notes that you find yourself singing and compare them.

High and low – useful words

Singers use the word **pitch** for how high or low notes are. The pitch of your voice depends on many things: your age and size, whether you are male or female, and how long you have been singing. The distance between the highest and lowest pitches you can comfortably sing is called your **range**. Opposite you will find exercises to improve your range and strengthen your voice. This will help your tone too.

About the singing exercises in this book
Some of the exercises below are shown in music notation. Don't worry if you don't read music yet. Your choir-trainer will work with you to help you learn what to sing. The exercises are described using some technical words. If they are unfamiliar, look them up in the index (pages 47–48).

 Increasing your range using sirens
Using *Ah*, *Mee* or *Hmm*, make siren sounds. Start with the note you found on page 8. Slide up to a higher note, back down to your starting note, down to a lower note, then back up to where you began. Gradually make the siren cover a wider range. Keep the sound even and the notes smoothly connected.

Finding and developing your range
Start with the note you found on page 8. Sing the three-note pattern below to *Ah*, *Mah* or *Yah*. After you sing it, move to the next note up. Keep going up as long as you can sing comfortably. Don't force your voice beyond this point.

Next, do the same thing but instead, move to the next note down, still using *Ah*, *Mah* or *Yah*. This time keep moving down for as long as you can sing comfortably.

 Producing a good tone
Hum a note, then open your mouth to a vowel sound: *Hmm–ee* for example. Sing up and down a five-note phrase (see page 10) using this vowel. Then sing the same exercise using a different vowel. When you hum, the sound should be resonant. You should feel vibrations behind your lips. When you open your mouth for the vowel, keep the sound in the same forward position.

 For the Light Blue pitch and range targets (page 44), you must sing a one-octave scale (see page 25) with even tone. To prepare for this, use the exercises above to develop your range. Then practise one-octave scales like the one below.

Diction

 Usually when you sing, you sing more than notes. There will be words too. How you pronounce words is called **diction**. Your diction must be clear so that listeners can hear and understand the words. When you sing you must open your mouth more than when you speak, and use your tongue and teeth more to pronounce letters. This may feel strange at first, but it helps your voice to **project** (reach the listeners properly) and keeps your diction clear.

Vowels and consonants

 All words are made up of vowels and consonants. Vowels are the letters A E I O and U. Consonants are all the other letters. Certain vowels will help you develop a resonant tone. Sing the vowels on the right to a scale (page 25) or a siren exercise (page 9).

Good vowel sounds for practice		
Ee	as in	me
Eh	as in	leg
Ah	as in	father
Aw	as in	door
Oo	as in	moon

Tongue twisters

 Get your mouth moving with some of the tongue twisters on the right. Using scale patterns, sing the tongue twister on one note, then move up a note in the scale, and so on.

> Red lorry yellow lorry
>
> Copper bottomed coffee pot
>
> Tip of the tongue and the lips and the teeth
>
> He mourns the aroma of Verona's arena

Projection of consonants

 Choose a well-known song. Whisper the words with as much energy as you can, so they can be understood at the other side of the room. Then sing the song quietly but make the consonants loud. It may feel strange, but it will make the words clear to your listeners. Note how much energy you need for your consonants here; aim to sing with this level of energy all the time.

Phrases

 Written or spoken words are grouped into sentences to make them easier to understand. In music, notes and words are grouped into **phrases**. Your choir trainer will explain the phrases in each piece you sing. (In written music they are often shown by long curved lines.) You sing each phrase as a single unit, often in a single breath (though follow your choir trainer's advice).

 When listening to you sing, your choir trainer will want to hear clear singing with crisp diction, pure vowels and even phrases. Whenever you sing, ask yourself:

- Am I singing clearly? Can listeners understand what I am singing?
- Am I opening my mouth wide and allowing the sound to project?
- Are my phrases clear and even?

 VOICE CARE TIP
Eat little and often. This gives you stamina to sing for long periods. If you have not had a proper meal before you sing, eat an energy bar half an hour before. This will keep your energy levels up during your rehearsal or performance.

For Light Blue level, you have to perform a verse of a song or hymn which you have prepared in advance. This shows your choir trainer how your voice is progressing. With your choir trainer, choose what you are going to sing and write the title and the verse in this box.

Preparing your song or hymn

 When you give your performance, your choir trainer or teacher will be listening for the following things:

 Good even tone (see pages 7–9)

 Clear diction and projection (see page 10)

 Continuity of notes in phrases (see page 10)

 Here are some hints to help you prepare for this:

- Practise regularly. This will improve your voice.

- Get used to forming each word by speaking them as well as singing them.

- Practise joining notes smoothly by sliding between them without singing the words.

- Without the words, sing 'ah' or hum, but this time don't slide between the notes. This will teach you where the tune goes and how it feels in your voice.

- Practise your hymn or song at home. This will give you confidence when you perform it.

 Listen carefully to yourself as you sing. Ask yourself:

- How is my breathing?
- Is the sound even throughout the verse?
- Are the words as clear as possible?

- Is my throat staying relaxed?
- Am I opening my mouth enough to project the sound?

Your performance

 When you feel ready, arrange with your choir trainer a time to give your performance. When you have finished, he or she will give you feedback about your singing. Your voice may need time to develop, so you may be asked to work on one particular aspect of your voice and perform your verse again later. If so, keep practising the exercises here as well as any others that your choir trainer suggests, and you will find that your singing improves.

 VOICE CARE TIP
Drink plenty of water before exercising your voice, and while singing. This will make your vocal folds flexible and moist, which is important for keeping your voice healthy.

Music basics

 To complete the 'Musical skills and understanding' targets for the Light Blue level of *Voice for Life*, you need to show that you know the names of notes, and that you can read and sing from a piece of simple music notation. Don't worry if you can't do this yet – you will find everything you need to know in this section of the book.

If you have achieved the White level of *Voice for Life* or sung in a choir before, you may already be familiar with some music words, signs and symbols. Try the puzzles below. If you can do most of them without too much trouble, you are ready for activities that start on page 14, which revise some of these words, signs and symbols and introduce new ones too. If you have problems, talk to your choir trainer, who may suggest that you look at Module B of the White level *Voice for Life* workbook before you start.

Singers use a special word for how high or low a note is. The letters are scrambled up below. Write the word in the box below.

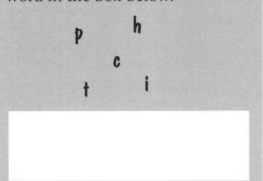

Musicians use the word **duration** to describe how long notes last. In the box below, circle the two notes with the same duration.

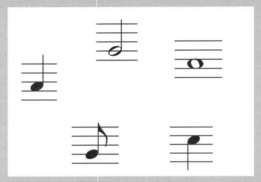

 There are four main types of voice in a choir, depending on their pitch. Write their names in the boxes below (some of the letters have been filled in for you). Then underline the name of the one you usually sing.

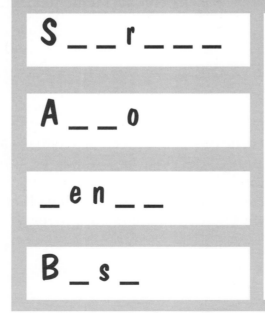

Connect each of the labels below to a sign or symbol on the music. One of them has been done for you.

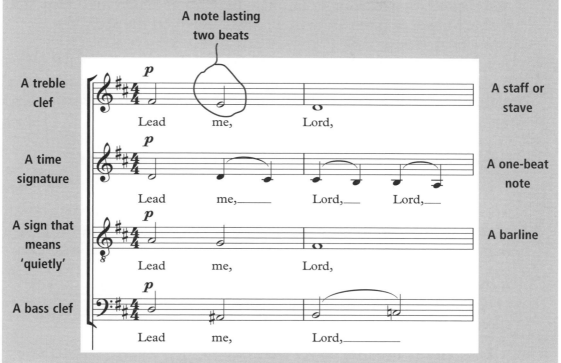

Odd one out 1

Music contains signs called repeats which tell you to sing part of the music twice. Circle the sign here which is *not* a type of repeat.

Odd one out 3

Circle the word below that is *not* the name of a part of a note.

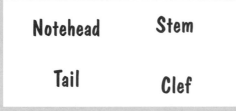

Odd one out 2

Music contains signs which tell you to jump to another part of the piece. Circle the sign below that does *not* tell you to do this.

Odd one out 4

Circle the sign below that does *not* tell you how loudly to sing.

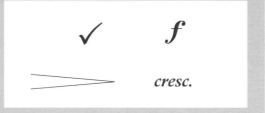

 In the music below, draw a line under the bars you have to sing twice.

Traditional French carol

Notes and their names

 Find a song or a piece of music that you know, which has the words and music written down. Sing it in your head or aloud. Look at the position of the notes. Notes that are higher in pitch are written higher up on the staff. Notes that are lower in pitch are written lower down on the staff.

 Notes are named after the first seven letters of the alphabet – A B C D E F G. After G, they start again at A. If you sing these notes in alphabetical order, they get higher in pitch. If you sing them in reverse alphabetical order, they get lower.

Going up, which note comes after E?		Going down, which note comes after C?	

 Notes are written on groups of five lines called a **staff** or **stave**. The curly sign at the beginning of each staff tells you which range of notes will be used on that staff. Most music for choirs has two different signs, called **clefs**.

A **treble clef** is used for higher notes. The sopranos and altos sing music in staves that begin with a treble clef.

A **bass clef** is used for lower notes. The basses will sing music in staves that begin with a bass clef.

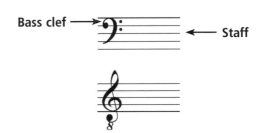

 Music for the tenors sometimes uses a bass clef, sometimes a type of treble clef like the one shown here.

 Notes in the treble clef
Here are the treble clef notes, with their letter names. Some of the notes are written on lines, and some are written in the spaces between the lines.

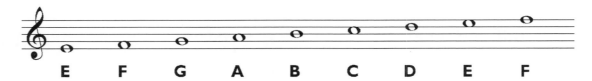

E   F   G   A   B   C   D   E   F

Above and below the staff
Some notes are higher or lower than the staff. Here are some of the most common ones.

The first two notes above the treble staff are **G** above the top line, and **A** on its own small line called a **leger line**.

Below the treble staff are **D** below the bottom line, and **C** on a leger line.

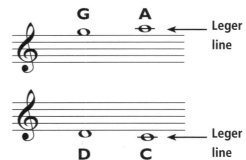

Notes in the bass clef
Here are the bass clef notes, with their letter names:

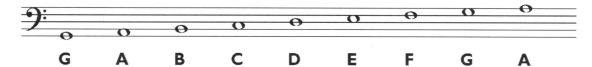

Above the bass staff are **B** above the top line, and **C** on a leger line.

Below the bass staff are **F** below the bottom line, and **E** on a leger line.

Where the staves meet
The C on a leger line *below* the treble staff is the same pitch as the C on a leger line *above* the bass clef. It is called **middle C** because it sits between the two staves and is found in the middle of a piano.

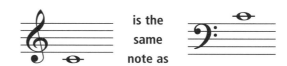

Note name reminders
In a group, or with your choir trainer, think of some sentences to help you remember the names of the notes. Divide the notes into two groups, notes on lines and notes in spaces, and make up a sentence for each one.

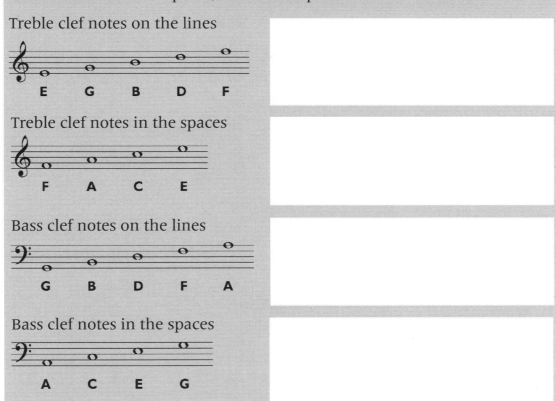

Notes and their names

Letter box

The name of each note on the staves below is written in the letter box on the right. Match each name in the box to a note on the staff. Use either the treble or the bass clef.

As you match each note, cross it out in the box. Some letters will be left. They spell the name of a composer

A G E C D C F G B A D F E H B

The composer is:

Word game

Here are some words written in notes. Can you read them? The first one has been done for you.

B E A D

___ ___ ___ ___

___ ___ ___ ___

Think of some words that use only the letters A to G. Write each one in notes below. (Make sure you write a clef on each staff first.)

If you think of more than four words, write the rest on another piece of paper. Then ask another choir member to 'read' your words.

A B C D E F G

As well as telling you about pitch, music also tells you about **duration** – how long and short notes are. This page and the next explain notes and rests of different lengths. To understand this, you need to know about counting beats of a pulse. If you need help with this, talk to your choir trainer or look at pages 18–22 of the White level workbook.

Note anatomy

Notes are made of different parts. The **notehead** is the oval part that sits on the line or in the space on the stave.

Stem ⟶   ⟵ Tail

Notehead ⟶

Stems and **tails** can point up or down. This doesn't affect the pitch or duration of the note. Notes with tails can be joined together with a longer line called a **beam**.

Tails can go up or down

Beam ↑

Here are some of the different notes you will see in written music. In 4/4,

A *semibreve* is a hollow note without a stem. It lasts four beats.

A *minim* is a hollow note with a stem. It lasts two beats.

A *crotchet* is a filled-in note with a stem. It lasts one beat.

A *quaver* is a filled-in note with a stem and a tail. It lasts half a beat.

Draw four crotchets in this box, two with stems up, two with stems down. How many beats in all?

In this box, draw four quavers, joined together with a beam. How many beats in all?

Draw two minims each on a line, and then two semibreves each in a space. How many beats?

Complete this sum:

𝅗𝅥 + 𝅗𝅥 =

Fill in the boxes:

𝅝 = [ ] crotchets   𝅝 = [ ] quavers

Rests

When not to sing

When you see a **rest**, you count its beats, but you don't sing anything. Each rest tells you how long to stay silent for. A rest lasts the same number of beats as the note of the same name. So a crotchet rest lasts the same length of time as a crotchet (normally one beat).

In the boxes below, write how long each rest lasts. (The first one has been done for you.)

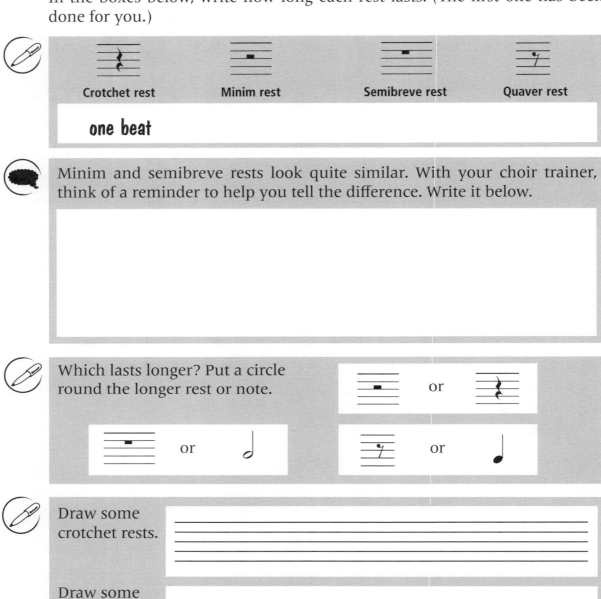

Crotchet rest   Minim rest   Semibreve rest   Quaver rest

one beat

Minim and semibreve rests look quite similar. With your choir trainer, think of a reminder to help you tell the difference. Write it below.

Which lasts longer? Put a circle round the longer rest or note.

Draw some crotchet rests.

Draw some quaver rests.

Draw one rest that lasts the same length of time as all of these notes:

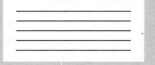

When you are singing, you count beats in your head so that you know where you are in the music and can keep in time with everybody else. (Your conductor will help you with this, but you still need to count carefully.) To help you count, beats in music are usually written in groups called **bars**.

Bars are separated from each other by vertical lines called **barlines**.

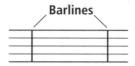

The end of a piece is shown by a **final barline** (one thin line and one thick).

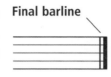

The end of a section in a piece is often shown by a **double barline** (two thin lines).

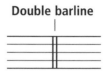

 Rests that last a bar or more
You need to count bars particularly carefully when you are not singing. Sometimes the music will tell you not to sing for several bars at a time.

A semibreve rest is used to show a full bar's rest in any time signature.

This sign tells you to rest for several bars. The number of bars is shown above the sign.

 Time signatures
At the start of a piece you will see a **time signature** – two numbers on the stave, written one above the other. The time signature applies for the whole piece, or until you see a different time signature.

Here are some time signatures you will see often. The top number tells you how many beats to count in each bar. The bottom number, 4, means each beat is a crotchet.

4/4 is also known as **common time**. The time signature for this is sometimes shown by a letter C at the start of the staff, instead of the two numbers.

The time signature 2/2 means there are two beats in each bar. The lower 2 means that each beat is a minim. So in 2/2, a crotchet lasts only half a beat.

 VOICE CARE TIP
Dairy products and some fruit juices cause congestion in the throat. This can make it feel as if you need to swallow a lot, cough, or clear your throat. Try to avoid chocolate, cheese, milk, and other dairy products before you sing. Drink water, not juice.

Counting

On the stave on the right, write the time signature for music with two crotchet beats in a bar.

Here, write the time signature for music with three crotchet beats in a bar.

Here, write the time signature for a piece that has two minim beats in a bar.

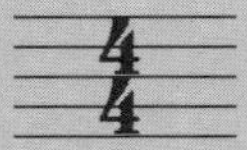

In a piece with this time signature, how many beats are there in a bar?

Draw one note which lasts for a whole 4/4 bar.

In a piece with this time signature, how many beats are there in a bar?

Draw one note which lasts for a whole 2/4 bar.

Think of some songs that you know. They could be songs that you have learned with your choir, chart music, or traditional songs. Sing each one in your head or aloud.

For each song, can you work out how many beats are in each bar? Think of a song that has four beats, one with three, and another with two beats in each bar.

Write the names of your songs here.

4 beats in a bar

3 beats in a bar

2 beats in a bar

Here are two incomplete bars in 4/4. How many minims do you need to add to complete the first bar? Write the missing note on the staff.

How many crotchets do you need to fill up the second bar? Write the missing notes on the staff.

Make a rhythm

A pattern of long and short notes is called a **rhythm**. Make your own rhythm on the staves below. First, decide whether your rhythm will be in 2/4, 3/4 or 4/4. Write the time signature at the start of the staff.

Then, look at the bars below. Find the ones with the correct number of beats for your time signature. Copy them, in any order, onto the staves. Then try making a rhythm with a different time signature.

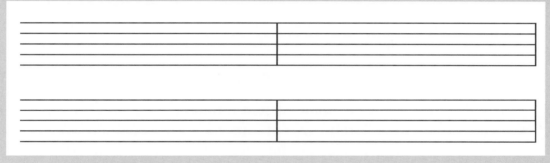

Clap your rhythm a few times. Clap louder on the first beat of each bar. Then clap it while other choir members listen. Can they tell you how many beats are in each bar? Can they tell which time signature you chose?

Sing the beginning of 'Three Blind Mice' as far as the word 'run'. As you sing, listen to the music as it rises and falls. Think about the distance between one note and the next.

While you sing, 'draw' the shape of the tune in the air. When it moves up, move your hand up. When it moves down, move your hand down. When it stays on the same note, keep your hand at the same height. Make the size of your hand movements match the size of the distances between the notes.

  Now sing the tune again. Draw its shape using dots above the words, one for each syllable. If the tune goes up, draw a higher dot. If it goes down, draw a lower dot. If it stays on the same note, draw a dot at the same level. Think about the distances between the notes as you sing and draw. Some of them have been done for you.

Three blind mice! Three blind mice! See how they run! See how they run!

 The distance between notes of two different pitches is called an **interval**. There are many different sizes of interval. In 'Three Blind Mice' some of the intervals are small steps, like the ones between the words 'Three' and 'blind' or 'See' and 'how'. Others are larger jumps, like the one between 'mice!' and 'Three' or 'run!' and 'See'.

Can you hear the largest interval in the music? Which two words is it between? Write them in the box below.

 The largest interval in 'Three Blind Mice' is between the words

	and	

 Sing 'Three Blind Mice' again. This time, look at the music. Think about the distance between each pitch and see how intervals of different sizes are shown by the position of the notes on the stave. Put a ring round the two notes that make the largest interval.

Measuring intervals
To measure the interval between two notes, you count the distance between them using the note names or numbers. Always include the notes you start and end on. Sing the interval between 'mice!' and 'See'. Use the note names, then the numbers 1 to 5. You have to sing from Middle C to the G above it.

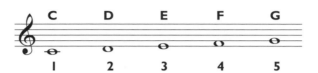

Including the notes you start and end on, how many notes do you sing to get from C to G? Write the answer in the box.

Try this on a keyboard too, using the white keys. Including the notes you start and end on, how many keys must you press to move by step from C to G?

You need to sing five notes, or press five white keys, to move upwards from C to G. An interval of five notes is called a fifth.

Using the notes names, and counting, sing from C to F. How many notes do you need? Can you guess the name of the interval? Write your answers here.

You need

[ ] notes to sing by step from C up to F.

An interval of four notes is called a [ ]

Many intervals, like the fifth and the fourth, are named after the number of steps they contain. Others have different names which give you more detailed information about them. Find out more over the page.

Why intervals are important
You need to practise singing intervals. When your muscles get used to the distances between pitches, you will be able to sing them easily when you see them in written music. It helps to remember intervals in well-known songs. There are a few suggestions below: you could try adding some of your own.

Interval of a fifth:
- The first two notes of 'Lavender's Blue'
- The first two notes of the theme to *Star Wars*

Interval of a fourth:
- The first two notes of 'Away in a manger'
- The first two notes of 'We wish you a merry Christmas'

More about intervals

 The first seven letters of the alphabet are used for names of notes. But there are more than seven notes, so these letters are repeated:

A B C D E F G A B C D E F G A B C D E F G A

 Therefore, there are several notes called A, and several called B, etc. The interval between one note and the next one of the same name, above or below it, is called an **octave**. So we say, for example, that one D and the next D (either above or below) are an **octave apart**. Can you sing this interval?

 On the music below, find two notes that are an octave apart, and draw a circle around each one.

Then find two notes that are two octaves apart, and draw a square around each one.

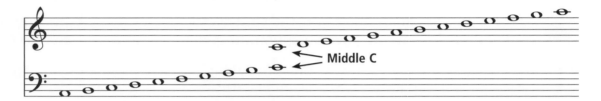
Middle C

Write either a treble or a bass clef on this staff. Then write two notes that are an octave apart. Whatever note you choose, one will be on a line and the other in a space.

Write a treble or bass clef on this staff. Then write a note that is an octave below the one shown. Will it be on a line or in a space?

 Singing by step

 At any comfortable pitch, slowly sing the first four bars of 'Three Blind Mice' a few times. Think about the notes that move by step. Draw them as you did on page 22, and listen carefully. Are all the steps the same size? (You may want to ask your choir trainer to help with this.)

Three blind mice! Three blind mice! See how they run! See how they run!

 The step between 'Three' and 'blind' and the step between 'blind' and 'mice' are the same size. But the step between 'they' and 'run' is smaller. You may need to sing and listen a few times to get used to the difference. The smaller step is an interval called a **semitone**. The larger step is an interval called a **tone**. Find out more on the opposite page.

Module B: Musical skills and understanding

The major scale

A **scale** is a chain of notes that moves by step, normally between two notes an octave apart. Most scales use steps of two different sizes – tones and semitones. A scale called a **major scale** uses a special pattern of tones and semitones. To sing a major scale from C to C going up, you sing these notes:

C D E F G A B C

 Sing this scale using the note names. It is a scale called **C major.** Then sing the notes in reverse. This is still a C major scale, but this time going down instead of up. Sing it with the numbers 1 to 8 going up, and 8 to 1 going down. Play it on a keyboard, or watch and listen as your choir trainer plays it. The C major scale uses only the white keys.

 Staircase puzzle

This staircase shows two Cs an octave apart, with stairs between them. Some of the notes in the scale of C major have been filled in. On the staircase, one stair equals a semitone; two stairs equal a tone. Remember that in a major scale some notes are a semitone apart; others are a tone apart.

 The missing note names are shown in the grey box. Can you put them on the stairs in the right places? To get from D to E, do you move up a semitone or a tone? To help you decide, sing the notes or look at a keyboard. (The shaded stairs represent the black keys on a keyboard.) When you have decided, put E on the chart. Then do the same with F and B.

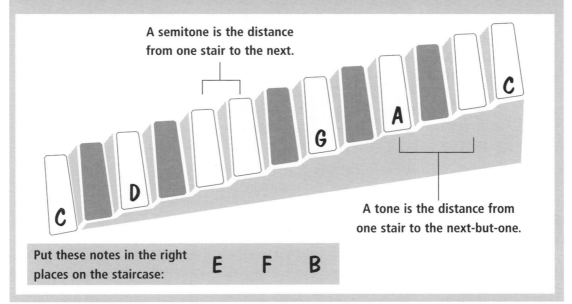

Put these notes in the right places on the staircase: E F B

 What is the fifth note in a C major scale called?

And what is the name of the eighth note?

In a major scale there are two semitone steps. One is between the third and fourth notes. The other is between the and the

Scales

 In a major scale, the pattern of tones and semitones, starting from the key note, is always:

Tone Tone Semitone Tone Tone Tone Semitone

On whatever note you begin a major scale, there must be a semitone between the third and fourth notes, and between the seventh and eighth. If you start on any note other than C, you need special notes (called **sharps** and **flats**). Only the scale of C major can be sung or played without using these notes. (On a keyboard, the black keys play sharps and flats.)

 The scale of G major
Write the first *six* notes of the scale of G major on the stairs chart below, starting with G on the bottom stair.

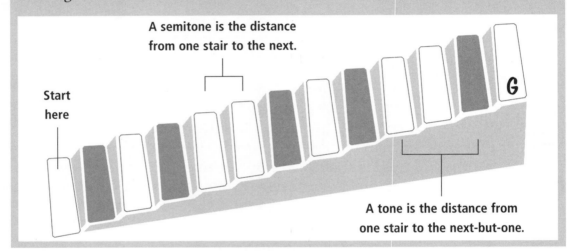

 In the scale of G major, the seventh note sits between F and G. This note is called F sharp.

In music, 'sharp' is shown by this symbol: ♯   On the stave, the sharp sign appears in front of the note.

F sharp

 A shorter way to write F sharp is F♯. Write F♯ on the stairs chart for G major.

 Sing, think, write
Find the note G. Starting there, sing five notes up the G major scale, then down again. Use the numbers 1 to 5, then the note names. What is the note a fifth above G? Write its name here.

 Starting on G, sing four notes up the G major scale, then back down again. Use the numbers 1 to 4, then the note names. What is the note a fourth above G? Write its name here.

 Starting on G, sing four notes down the G major scale, then up again. Use the numbers 8 down to 5, then the note names. What is the note a fourth below G? Write its name here.

You can start a major scale on any note. Some major scales need sharps, some need flats. No major scale needs both sharps and flats.

 The scale of F major
On the chart below, write in the first *three* notes of the scale of F major. Use the same pattern of tones and semitones as you did for the C major and G major charts. Start by writing F on the bottom stair.

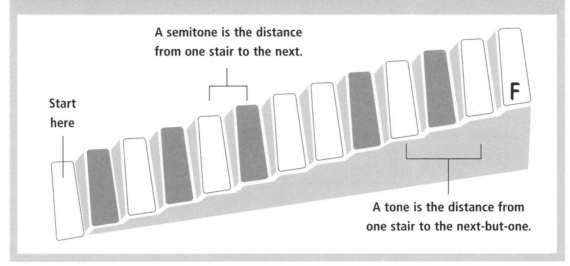

A semitone is the distance from one stair to the next.

Start here

A tone is the distance from one stair to the next-but-one.

F

 In the scale of F major, the fourth note sits between A and B. This note is called B flat.

In music, 'flat' is shown by this symbol: ♭

The flat sign appears in front of the note.

B flat

 A shorter way to write B flat is B♭. Write B♭ on your chart for F major, then fill in the rest of the notes. Do you remember where to put the other semitone?

 Sing, think, write
Find the note F. Starting there, sing five notes up the F major scale, then down again. Use the numbers 1 to 5, then the note names. What is the note a fifth above F? Write its name here.

 Starting on F, sing four notes up the F major scale, then back down again. Use the numbers 1 to 4, then the note names. What is the note a fourth above F? Write its name here.

Starting on F, sing four notes down the F major scale, then up again. Use the numbers 8 down to 5, then the note names. What is the note a fourth below F? Write its name here.

What is the name of the the note you sing on the number 7? Write its name here.

Keys and key signatures

If a piece of music uses the notes of the scale of G major (in any order), we say that it is **in the key of** G major (or sometimes just 'in the key of G' or 'in G').

The note G is so important in the scale and key of G major that it has a special name: the **tonic**. The name of the tonic is always the same as the name of its scale and key. So the tonic of F major is F, and the tonic of C major is C. Tunes in major keys usually end on their tonic, and often begin on their tonic too.

Write the letter name of the tonic of E major in this box.

Write the letter name of the tonic of B flat major in this box.

Because music in G major uses the notes of the G major scale, it is likely to contain F sharps. Sometimes you will see a sharp sign in front of each F. But usually a sharp sign is written at the beginning of each staff to show that every F is an F sharp, and that the piece is in G major. This is called a **key signature**. It means you don't have to write a sharp in front of every F.

This is how the key signature for G major is written in the treble and bass clefs.

G major key signature (treble clef)

G major key signature (bass clef)

If a piece is in the key of F major, then usually a flat sign is written at the start of each staff to show that every B is a B flat. The flat sign is written so that the hollow part of it is on the line or space where B is written.

This is how the key signature for F major is written in the treble and bass clefs.

F major key signature (treble clef)

F major key signature (bass clef)

Because the scale and key of C major has no sharps or flats, there are no sharps or flats in the key signature for C major.

Key signatures have *either* sharps *or* flats *or* neither. No major scale or major key signature has both sharps and flats.

On the staff below, write either a treble or a bass clef. Then add the key signature of either G major or F major. Next, write the notes of the major scale of your chosen key. Start on the tonic nearest the bottom of the staff and go up until you reach the tonic again. Remember you don't need to put any sharp or flat signs in front of the notes themselves, because you have already written the key signature for your chosen key.

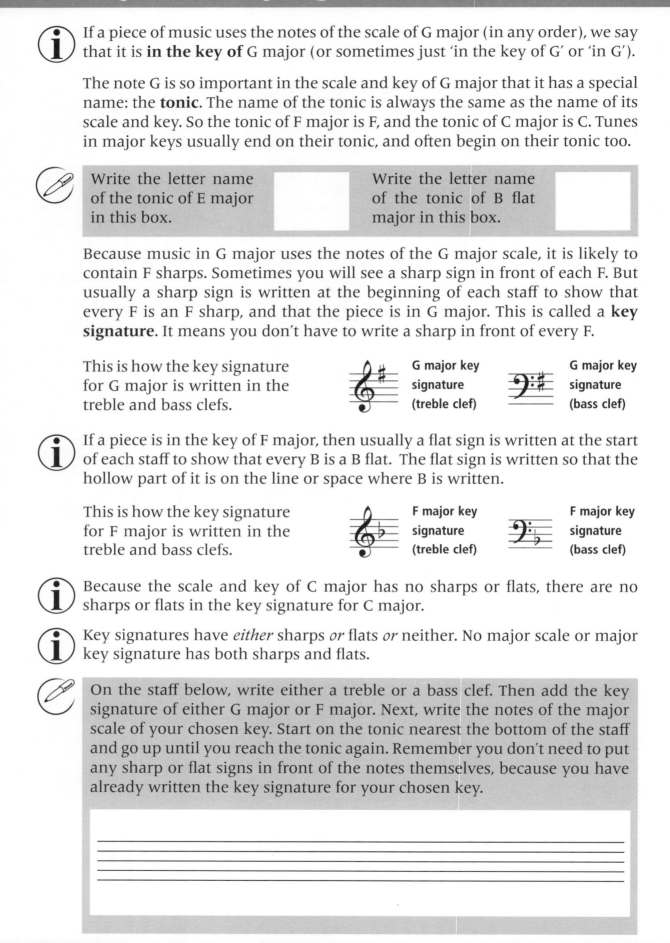

Module B: Musical skills and understanding

Linked keys
Look at the key signatures below. Can you work out what keys they represent, and link them to their tonic notes?

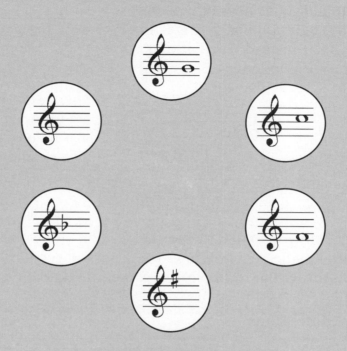

Now try the same thing with the bass clef.

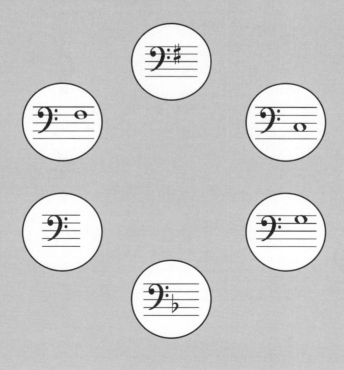

VOICE CARE TIP
You need to be reasonably fit in order to sing well. Consider taking some form of
regular exercise. Anything that keeps you active for around 20 minutes is good.

Accidentals

 Sometimes composers want to use notes that are not included in a key signature. To do this, they put sharp or flat signs directly in front of notes. Sharp, flat or natural signs placed immediately before notes are called **accidentals**.

For example, a flat sign immediately before a B tells you not to sing B, but to sing B flat instead. The flat makes the note a semitone lower.

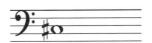

A sharp sign before a note makes it a semitone higher. For example, a sharp before a C tells you to sing a note a semitone higher, so C sharp.

Another sign that you may see placed in front of notes is a **natural** sign.

 Natural sign

This sign tells you to sing the normal version of the note, that is, the one with a plain letter name, such as B or C. These normal versions of notes are sometimes called **naturals**. For example, B is sometimes known as **B natural**.

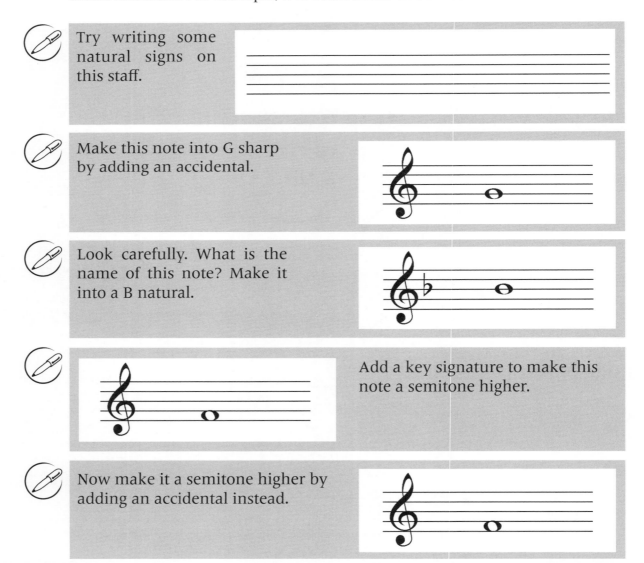

Try writing some natural signs on this staff.

Make this note into G sharp by adding an accidental.

Look carefully. What is the name of this note? Make it into a B natural.

Add a key signature to make this note a semitone higher.

Now make it a semitone higher by adding an accidental instead.

Accidentals

 Accidentals don't only apply to the note that immediately follows them. They also apply to any other note of the same name that appears later **within the same bar**. For example, if you see an F with a sharp in front of it, and there is another F later in the same bar, then both of the Fs become F sharps.

In the example below, the sharp sign makes the second and third Gs into G sharps. But then the natural sign, just before the fourth G, cancels out the sharp sign, so the fourth G is a G natural.

In this example, what is the name of the first note?

What is the name of the second note?

 Add one accidental to make all of these Fs into F sharps.

 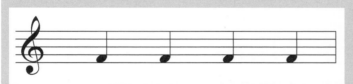 Add one accidental to make only one of these Fs into an F sharp.

 Add two accidentals to make only one of these Fs into an F sharp.

  Add one accidental to make all these notes F naturals.

If you need help with these accidentals, ask your choir trainer.

Dynamics

 Printed music often gives you clues about how loudly to sing. It may tell you to sing very loudly, very quietly, or somewhere in between. These instructions are called **dynamics**. Dynamics are often written in Italian. Sometimes letters are used instead – these are short for the Italian words.

p	stands for	**piano** (say *pee-ah-no*)	which means	**quietly**
f	stands for	**forte** (say *for-tay*)	which means	**loudly**
pp	stands for	**pianissimo**	which means	**very quietly**
ff	stands for	**fortissimo**	which means	**very loudly**

The Italian word *mezzo* (say *met-so*) means 'half' or 'middle'.

mp	stands for	**mezzo piano**	which means	**fairly quietly**
mf	stands for	**mezzo forte**	which means	**fairly loudly**

 Here are some dynamic markings. Starting with the quietest, can you join them up in order of volume?

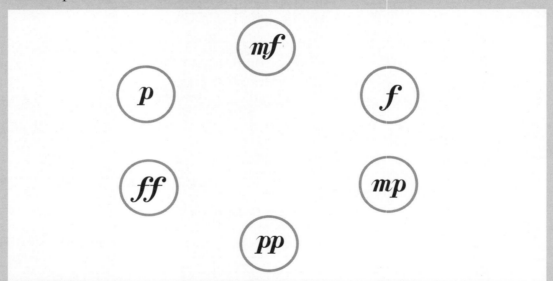

 You will often see a dynamic marking at the beginning of a piece, and then different dynamics later in the piece, which tell you to change your volume. Some dynamics tell you to change your volume *gradually*, that is, to get louder or quieter bit by bit.

cresc.	stands for	**crescendo** (say *cresh-endo*)	which means	**get gradually louder**
dim.	stands for	**diminuendo**	which means	**get gradually quieter**
decresc.	stands for	**decrescendo**	which also means	**get gradually quieter**

 VOICE CARE TIP
Do you wake up in the morning with a sore throat? This could be due to a hot, dry atmosphere or household dust or pollen. Drink plenty of water and keep your room well ventilated.

Module B: Musical skills and understanding

Dynamics

 The signs below are sometimes used instead of these words. (These signs are sometimes known as hairpins.)

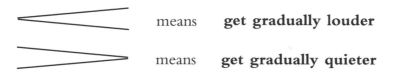

 In each of the gaps below, write a hairpin sign. To change from the first dynamic to the second dynamic, which hairpin do you need?

mp   *pp*

f   *ff*

p   *mf*

 Writing dynamics

Add dynamic markings to the rhythm below. It should begin fairly quietly. The second bar should become gradually quieter. The third bar should be very quiet. There should be a crescendo throughout the fourth and fifth bars and the sixth should be forte. Write each marking underneath the appropriate part of the rhythm.

When you have finished, clap the rhythm, following the dynamics.

 Choosing your own dynamics

 Find one of the rhythms that you made for the puzzle on page 21 and clap it. Put a dynamic marking at the beginning of your rhythm. Then add other dynamics to your rhythm – which parts of the rhythm do you think should be loud? Which should be quiet?

Then ask another student or choir member to clap your rhythm, following the dynamics.

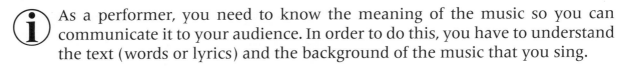
Understanding the music we sing

As a performer, you need to know the meaning of the music so you can communicate it to your audience. In order to do this, you have to understand the text (words or lyrics) and the background of the music that you sing.

Did you know that somebody wrote the music you sing? If you painted a picture, it would be an original – no one else would ever have painted that picture before. In the same way, music has to be written or created. A person who writes music is called a **composer**.

For your Light Blue target, you will need to find out about some of the music that you sing. For one of the pieces, you will be asked to:

- name the composer
- read the words aloud (if they are in English or another language that you know well)
- find out when the composer lived (the musical period or century)
- answer questions on the meaning of the words and mood of the music

How do I find out who wrote the piece?
The composer's name may be on the front cover of the music, or on the first page (usually under the title on the right). If somebody else wrote the words, you may find their name too.

For some tunes (particularly old ones) nobody knows the composer's name. Many old tunes were not written down. People learned them and passed them on so that eventually no-one knew who wrote them or where they came from. This is shown by the words below, instead of the name of a composer:

Music: anon.   This means the composer is anonymous (unknown).

Music: trad.   This means the music is a traditional tune.

On the printed music, you may also see the name of an **arranger** (sometimes shortened to 'arr.'). An arranger is someone who has taken an existing piece of music (either by a known or an anonymous composer, or a traditional tune) and created a new version. For example, it may be a version for different instruments or voices, or a simpler version, or a shorter or longer one.

How do I find out when the composer lived?
Sometimes the composer's dates are shown on the music. This may be in a paragraph about the composer, or in brackets after his or her name. If there are no dates on the printed music, try looking in the places listed below:

- Programme notes from concerts – these often contain information about the composer of each piece.
- Music encyclopaedias and dictionaries – try a library. (For composers who are still alive, the other sources mentioned here may be more useful.)
- CD booklets or download details
- Music magazines often contain articles on composers – try *Church Music Quarterly*, *BBC Music Magazine* and *Classic FM Magazine*.
- The Internet – put the composer's name into a search engine.

Look at these examples and answer the questions.

Lavender's Blue

Music: trad

Arr. Dave E. Burnsell

Do we know who composed this piece?

Has the piece been arranged by anyone?

AVE, VERUM

CORPUS

·

W. A. Mozart

Who is the composer of the music?

Has the piece been arranged by anyone?

VOICE CARE TIP

Your whole body is involved in singing, not just your mouth. The muscles need regular exercise. Sprinters do not run at top speed all the time – they exercise their whole bodies to get fit enough to perform at their best. In the same way, singers need regular vocal work-outs. Aim for sessions of about 5 – 10 minutes, several times a week, so that your muscles are strong enough to respond to the demands of the music that you sing.

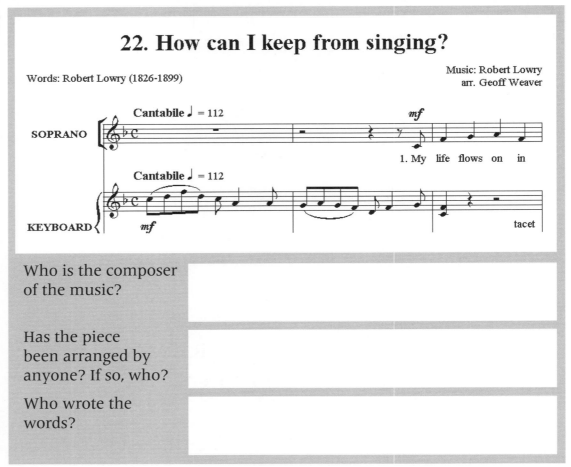

Who is the composer of the music?	
Has the piece been arranged by anyone? If so, who?	
Who wrote the words?	

(i) ***How do I find out what some of the words mean and how to pronounce them?***
You could ask your choir trainer or teacher, or look in a dictionary for a definition. If the words are in a language you don't understand, there may be a translation written somewhere on the printed music. If not, you could try a language dictionary, or ask someone you know who speaks the language.

(i) ***How do I find out what the mood of the music is?***
Listen to the music. How does it make you feel? What does it make you think of? Why do you think the music makes you feel that way? Look at the words too – they are a clue to the mood of the piece.

(•) With your choir trainer, decide on a few pieces of music to research. For each piece, answer the questions opposite. If you like, take copies of the page so that you have enough for all the pieces you research.

VOICE CARE TIPS

(i) *Tiredness affects your voice. When you are tired it takes more effort to breathe, which can lead to vocal strain. Tiredness also makes your throat drier, which makes the voice sound strained and lacking in resonance. Get plenty of rest before you sing!*

(i) *The chlorine in the water in swimming pools can dry out your vocal mechanism. Try to avoid swimming immediately before you sing. If you cannot avoid this, make sure you drink plenty of water once you have finished swimming.*

What is the title of the piece?

Who wrote the music?

When did the composer live? (Give dates, musical period or century.)

Read the text aloud. Do you find any of the words difficult to pronounce? If so, write them here.

Are you unsure of the meaning of any of the words? If so, find out what they mean and write the definition next to each word here.

Word	Definition

Explain simply in your own words what you think the whole text means.

What is the mood of the music?

How did you find this information? Where did you look?

You may photocopy this page

Singing as part of a choir

 As a singer, you need to practise individually and work on your own voice and musical ability in order to improve. However, you are also part of a choir. This means that you are part of a team. Being part of a team is much easier and more enjoyable if all the members of the team co-operate and take part.

In a sports team, it is important that all the members participate. Otherwise, the other members have to work harder and will get tired more quickly. It is the same for a choir.

Choir members must be reliable and committed. Choir trainers need to know that singers will arrive on time and be focused in rehearsals and performances. They also need to know in advance if a singer is going to be absent.

It is also important that everyone sings when they are expected to. At the beginning of a piece, or when there are rests in your part, concentrate and watch the conductor so that you are ready to start singing when required.

 Ask yourself the following questions. Write the answers here, then ask your choir trainer to comment on them.

Am I a reliable member of my choir? How could I improve my reliability?

What do I do if I find I am unable to attend a rehearsal or performance?

How do I get ready and focused to sing at the start of a rehearsal or performance?

Am I a helpful member of my choir? How could I be more helpful?

Do I contribute to the sound of the whole choir? How could I do better?

This module of *Voice for Life* is about what it means to sing in a choir and what your choir means to you, other singers, and the people who listen to it. The answers to these questions will be different for each choir and singer, so there are no formal tests for this module. Instead, your choir trainer will ask you to think about the topics below one at a time, and write the answers to the questions in the boxes.

Before you start writing, it may help to talk to other singers or do some internet research. Your choir trainer will look at your answers and may chat with you about them. You may be asked to follow up some points or answer more questions. To complete this module for Light Blue, you have to finish at least *two* of the topics. Topic 3 is for church choirs only.

Topic 1: The gift of music

Think about the idea of a gift – something you give or receive. This could be something material (like a birthday or Christmas gift), or emotional (like friendship), or something living (like a pet or a plant). You may have other gifts too, such as a talent for sport or science or drawing.

Now think about music. It is a gift in two ways. It is a talent given to many people, enabling them to perform music well. And it is a gift given to listeners whenever performers make music.

When and how did you first become involved in music?

How has music become important in your life?

How do you plan to develop the gift of music in the future? What help do you think you might need for this?

Topic 2: The power of music

Think of the many things music can make you feel. Some pieces make you feel joyful, others make you sad.

Think about the sort of feelings music can inspire. List them in this box.

Choose a piece of music that is special to you – a 'powerful' piece that causes strong feelings. In this box, write its name and describe why it's powerful.

Music's power is used in many different ways in the wider world, such as advertising or sports. In the box below, write some examples of the ways the power of music is used.

List some ways in which the power of your own singing and music making has affected other people.

Topic 3: Places of worship

Think about a place that is familiar to you (for example your office, your bedroom, your classroom). Think about the people who use it, and how the layout and the furniture it contains reflects their needs and lives.

Look around the church where your choir sings. Think about important places inside and outside the building, and also about the church furniture (altar, font and so on). List some of these features in the box below.

Now choose three of the church features from the box above. Write each of them in the box below. Say what it is used for, when it is used, and by whom.

Find out about the history of your church. When was it built? Can you list some of the people involved in its creation and upkeep?

On this page and the next, you can find many of the signs and symbols you will see in the music you sing. Most of them are described in this book. For more detailed explanations, go to the pages listed under each heading.

Notes in the treble clef (page 14)

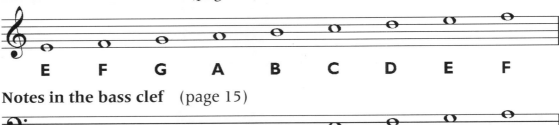

E F G A B C D E F

Notes in the bass clef (page 15)

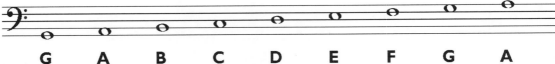

G A B C D E F G A

Notes above and below the staves (pages 14 and 15)

G   A
   ← Leger line
D   C

B   C
F   E

Notes on a keyboard

C D E F G A B C D E F G A B C D E F G A B C D E F G A B

Note anatomy (page 17)

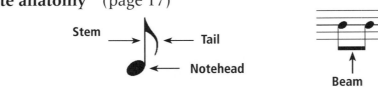

Stem →   ← Tail
    ← Notehead
Beam

Note lengths (page 17)

♪ or Quaver
(half a crotchet beat)

♩ or Crotchet
(one beat)

♩ or Minim
(two crotchet beats)

𝅝 Semibreve
(four crotchet beats)

Rests (pages 18 and 19)

Quaver rest   Crotchet rest   Minim rest   Semibreve rest or one bar rest   Multiple bar rest (rest for the number of bars shown)

Counting notes in groups (page 19)

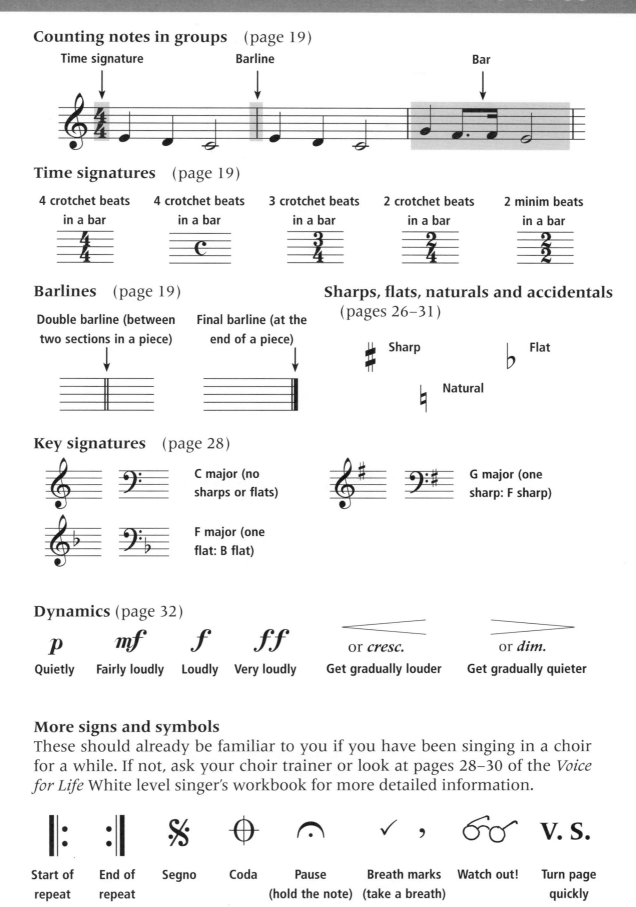

Time signature   Barline   Bar

Time signatures (page 19)

4 crotchet beats in a bar	4 crotchet beats in a bar	3 crotchet beats in a bar	2 crotchet beats in a bar	2 minim beats in a bar
4/4	**C**	**3/4**	**2/4**	**2/2**

Barlines (page 19)

Double barline (between two sections in a piece)

Final barline (at the end of a piece)

Sharps, flats, naturals and accidentals (pages 26–31)

♯ Sharp   ♭ Flat

♮ Natural

Key signatures (page 28)

C major (no sharps or flats)

G major (one sharp: F sharp)

F major (one flat: B flat)

Dynamics (page 32)

p — Quietly

mf — Fairly loudly

f — Loudly

ff — Very loudly

⟨ or *cresc.* — Get gradually louder

⟩ or *dim.* — Get gradually quieter

More signs and symbols

These should already be familiar to you if you have been singing in a choir for a while. If not, ask your choir trainer or look at pages 28–30 of the *Voice for Life* White level singer's workbook for more detailed information.

Start of repeat	End of repeat	Segno	Coda	Pause (hold the note)	Breath marks (take a breath)	Watch out!	Turn page quickly
‖:	:‖	𝄋	⊕	⌢	✓ ,	👓	V. S.

Targets

These are the targets for the Light Blue level of *Voice for Life*. As you work through this book, you will learn to do all the things below. This section is a record of your progress, so write your name here.

_____

Each time you achieve a target, your choir trainer will sign the box and record the date. There is no time limit to complete the targets. It is more important to learn everything thoroughly than to rush to finish the book. Your choir trainer will make sure that you make steady progress so that when you finish the book you are prepared for the next level.

When all the boxes are signed, you have successfully completed Light Blue level. Your choir trainer will sign the declaration on the inside back cover of the book, where you can also find out what happens next.

Module A: Using the voice well
The singer understands the need for regular practice and:

	Signed:	Date:
• understands how to stand and sit while singing, and demonstrates good posture in rehearsals and performances.		
• demonstrates good breath management by singing with an even tone.		
• has found a comfortable register in which to sing and can demonstrate this by singing with even tone an ascending and descending scale of an octave.		
• sings with clear diction, producing good pure vowels and clear consonants.		
• can sing a verse of a hymn or song with clear diction and projection, good even tone and continuity between the notes of a phrase.		

Module B: Musical skills and understanding
The singer has completed the theory section of the Light Blue workbook and demonstrates that he/she knows and understands:

	Signed:	Date:
• the pitch names of the notes of the treble clef (or staff).		
• the basic note values and their equivalent rests.		

Module B *continued*

Signed: Date:

- the concept of scales and the pattern of the major scale.

- the concept of accidentals.

- the key signatures of C, F and G major.

- the concept of bars and time signatures (2/4, 3/4, 4/4, 2/2).

- the basic dynamic markings (listed on page 32).

The singer has read and understood the music theory in Module B and can:

Signed: Date:

- sing back a simple melody, which will be played twice. The key chord and tonic will first be sounded and the pulse indicated.

- clap back a simple rhythm. The pulse will first be indicated and the test played twice.

- sing, unaccompanied, a one-octave major scale (ascending and descending). The key chord and tonic will first be sounded.

- tap the pulse of a passage of music in 2 or 3 time. The passage will be played twice. On the second playing the singer should tap the pulse and stress where the strong beats fall, then say whether it is in 2 or 3 time.

- clap or sing, on one note, a simple rhythm from sight.

- sing a simple step-wise melody from sight on any vowel. The key chord and tonic will first be sounded.

The singer has completed the 'Music basics' puzzles on pages 12 and 13.

Signed: Date:

MODULE C: Repertoire

The singer has completed the section on repertoire in the workbook and knows how to take a piece of music and:

	Signed:	Date:
• find out who composed the piece and when.		
• read aloud the text of a piece (in English only).		
• make simple observations about the meaning of the text and the mood of the piece.		

MODULE D: Belonging to the choir

The singer:

	Signed:	Date:
• is a committed and punctual member of the choir who informs the choir trainer before being absent from rehearsals, services or concerts.		
• is focused during rehearsals, services or concerts.		
• understands that he/she is singing as part of a group and that he/she needs to contribute to the overall sound.		

MODULE E: Choir in context

The singer has completed at least two of the three topic sheets on pages 39-41.

	Signed:	Date:
• Topic 1: The gift of music		
• Topic 2: The power of music		
• Topic 3: Places of worship		

Important words used in this book are explained briefly here. For a more detailed explanation, go to the pages listed under each heading. Any word in **bold** type also has an entry elswhere in this index.

A few topics in this book are explained more fully in the *Voice for Life* White level workbook. So WL24 after the entry for **Alto** means you will find more information about this topic on page 24 of the White level workbook.

Accidental a sign placed in front of a note, indicating that its pitch is to be altered   30–31

Alto the second highest voice in a choir   WL24

Arranger the person who creates a different version of an existing piece of music   34

Bar written music is divided into bars; each bar contains a certain number of **beats**   19

Barline a line dividing one **bar** from the next   19

Bass the lowest voice in a choir   WL24

Bass clef a sign at the start of a **staff** showing that the music contains low notes   14, 15

Beam a line joining two or more short notes   17

Beat music is divided into units called beats; beats are grouped into **bars**   17, 19, WL18–22

Breathing   7   **Breathing exercises**   7

C major a major **key**   25

Choir a co-ordinated group of singers   38

Choir trainer someone who trains and develops a choir   WL13

Clef a sign at the beginning of a **staff** showing the range of notes used on that staff   14

Closed score a **score** with more than one **part** on each staff   WL24

Common time 4/4 or four crotchet beats in each bar   19

Composer the person who writes or creates a piece of music   34

Conductor someone who directs your choir in rehearsals and performances   WL13

Consonants all the letters of the alphabet except A, E, I, O and U   10

Crotchet a note which usually lasts for one **beat**   17

Diction the way words are pronounced and expressed   10

Double barline a double line showing the end of a piece or a section of a piece   19

Duration how long notes last   17

Dynamics instructions which tell musicians how loud or quiet music should be   32, 33

F major a major **key**   27

Flat a sign indicating that a note is to be made a **semitone** lower   27–31

G major a major **key**   26, 28

Humming singing with closed mouth   7, 8

Hymn notation a type of **closed score**   WL24

Interval the difference in pitch between two notes   22–24

Key a selection of notes, taken from a **scale**, around which a piece of music is based   28

Key signature signs (**sharps** or **flats**) at the start of a piece which indicate its **key**   28

Larynx the voice-box (in the neck) which produces vocal sounds   8

Major key a **key** which uses the notes of a **major scale**   28

Major scale   25

Minim a note which lasts the length of two **crotchets**   17

Mood The atmosphere of a piece of music   36

Natural the 'ordinary' letter name version of a note – not a **sharp** or **flat**   30

Notation how music is written down   12–19, 42–43, WL15–31

Notehead the oval part of a note that sits on a line or in a space   17

Note names notes are named after the first seven letters of the alphabet   14–15

Octave the **interval** between one note and the next one of the same name above or below it   24